Research Re[search] to Knock Your Teacher's Socks Off!

by
Nancy Polette

Pieces of
Learning

©1997 Nancy Polette
Pieces of Learning, Publisher

www.piecesoflearning.com
CLC0206
ISBN 1-880505-56-8

Printed in the U.S.A.

Research Reports to Knock Your Teacher's Socks Off!
By Nancy Polette

Imagine it is a typical research report day. You look around the room and see most of the class asleep. The teacher is nodding off, too. Why? Because listening to copied enclyclopedia reports of Australian animals is not the most exciting way you can think of to spend a morning. Finally it is your turn. You put on your bush hat, greet the class with "g'day" (Australia for hello), put a taped drumbeat on the tape player and launch into a WOMBAT CHANT!

FACTS ABOUT WOMBATS

Have a pouch
Tough hide
Long fur
Sharp claws
Small ears
Whiskers
These are just a few . . .

Vegetable eaters
Carry young
Good pets
Dig burrows
Yellow-black
Night creatures
Eat leaves, too.
From near and far . . .
Here they are . . .
Facts about wombats!

Your classmates have picked up the beat. They clap along to the rhythm. When you are finished there are cries of "Do it again!" This time they chant along. The teacher joins in, too. Your report is the hit of the morning and sure to get an "A." How did you do it? It was easy. You simply organized your information in a new way.

With easy directions and specific examples, this book will show you many different ways to organize information on animals, people, places and events, making research both fun and rewarding.

Turn the pages to find models that appeal to you. Follow the directions and you are sure to "knock your teacher's socks off" with your next research report!

REPORTING ON

ANIMALS

REPORTING ON ANIMALS

WHAT TO DO: Create a Data Bank About the Animal

Data Bank - Wombat

Lives
Australia
in a burrow
Tasmania

Eats
roots
vegetables
leaves

What it Does
carries its young in a pouch
makes an affectionate pet
digs large earth burrows
comes out only at night

What it Has
a pouch
tough hide
long fur
sharp claws
small ears
whiskers

Looks Like
2-3 feet long
yellow/black color
furry possum

Transfer the Data Bank Information to this pattern:

FACTS ABOUT WOMBATS
(List six facts from the Data Bank)

1. _____
2. _____
3. _____
4. _____
5. _____
6. _____

These are just a few.
(Now list seven more facts from the Data Bank)

1. _____
2. _____
3. _____
4. _____
5. _____
6. _____
7. _____, too!

From near and far
Here they are
Facts about wombats.

Example:
Wombat Chant
Facts about wombats
Has a pouch
Tough hide
Long fur
Sharp claws
Small ears
Whiskers
These are just a few.
Vegetable eater
Carries young
Good pet
Digs burrows
Yellow-black
Night creature
Eat leaves, too.
From near and far,
Here they are,
Facts about wombats!

2

AUSTRALIAN ANIMAL CHANT

This variation describes several animals.

Here's another one!

Australian animals!

Duck-billed

Platypus

Feathered

Emu

Scaly

Lizard

These are just a few

Prickly spined

Echidna

Wild dog

Dingo

Pockets

Kangaroo

What a mixed up zoo!

Stand and shout

Bring them out

Australian animals!

I like spiders!

Crab spiders

Ground spiders

Jumping spiders

Stick spiders

Wolf spiders

Tarantulas

These are just a few!

In a web

Underground

On a flower

In the house

Between the leaves

In the grass

Trapdoor spiders, too!

Stand and shout,

Bring them out

I like spiders!

Use the Data Bank and Chant Pattern for any animal!

The first list names different spiders. The second list tells where each is found.

3

MORE CHANTS

A
N
I
M
A
L
S

Data Bank - Alligator

Eats	Has	Does
fish	thick body	makes nest of grass
snakes	80 sharp teeth	lays 50 eggs at a time
dogs	short, strong legs	grows about one foot a year
turtles	tough skin	rests under water in winter
frogs	powerful tail	lives 50-60 years

Lives	Looks Like
Southeast United States	lizard
China	18 feet long
Central America	450-550 pounds
South America	dull gray or dark olive color

—Anotther variation —

An Alligator Chant

Facts about alligators:

Eats fish

And snakes

Thick body

Sharp teeth

Tough skin

Like a lizard

These are just a few

Strong legs

Lays eggs

Lives 60 years

Dull gray

18 ft

500 lbs

Nest in grass, too.

From near and far

Here they are

Facts about ALLIGATORS!

(All information came from the data bank)

Have You Seen Eggs?

Robin's eggs

In a nest.

Snake eggs

In a hole.

Crocodile eggs

In the swamp.

THESE ARE JUST A FEW

Ostrich eggs

Along the dunes.

Turtle eggs

In the sand.

Penguin eggs

In the snow.

Easter Eggs, Too.

Stand and shout

Bring them out

WE'VE SEEN EGGS!

THE PATTERN

HAVE YOU SEEN _____

_____

_____

_____

_____

_____

These are just a few

_____

_____

_____

_____

_____

Stand and shout

Bring them out

We've seen _____

4

© Pieces of Learning

THE NEVER-EVER REPORT

You should never-ever *kiss an alligator* because *you might get your head stuck in his huge mouth that holds about eighty teeth.*

And you should definitely never-ever *try to play tag with an alligator* because *he can shoot out of the water like a missile and bolt forward in short bursts on his strong legs.*

But you can *ask an alligator if his great-great grandfather knew Tyrannosaurus Rex* because *alligators lived at the same time that dinosaurs did.*

– The Model –

You should never-ever _____ because you might

_____.

And you should definitely never-ever _____

because _____ and _____.

But you can _____ because _____.

– *Use the model for any Animal Report* –

You should never-ever *ask a wolf to live in a condominium because a wolf needs a home that consists of anywhere from 40 to 100 square miles of territory.*

And you should definitely never-ever *run a marathon race against a wolf because a wolf has such great endurance that he can lope all night long if he has to.*

But you can *get advice from a wolf about having a successful marriage because a wolf mates for life!*

5

THE TEN FACT RIDDLE POEM

Here is a poem about a hill country creature that contains ten facts. The name of the creature is given in the last line of the poem. Use this poem as a model. Find interesting information about another hill country creature and include the facts you find in a riddle poem.

WHAT IS IT ???

This riddle poem, if you're a whiz,
Will tell you what this creature is.

How big is it do you suppose?
32 inches from its tail to its nose?

It has long legs and sharp, sharp claws.
Enough to give a hunter pause.

A favorite food is fresh crayfish,
But frogs can make a tasty dish.

Its home is in a hollow tree,
Its coarse gray hair is hard to see.

Around its tail are black ring hoops,
It robs bird's nests and chicken coops.

If you don't guess this creature soon,
I'll tell you. . . it's a wild RACCOON.

6

ABOUT LIONS
A Ten Fact Riddle Poem

Guess what the animal is before reading the last verse.

It's true, you know.
This creature can
Both smell and hear
Better than man.

It has strong jaws
And sharp, sharp teeth,
For cutting through
The toughest meat.

It lives in grasslands
You will see,
With others near
For company.

In tall, tall grass
The creature hides,
With others in
The groups called prides.

The female hunts
And brings home meat,
Her lazy mate
Gets first taste treat.

LIONS do not
Eat bananas
But find prey
In tall Savannahs.

— *A Ten Fact Riddle Poem Example* —

It lives in fields
And under eaves
In attics, barns
And piles of leaves.

_____
_____
_____
_____

_____
_____
_____
_____

_____
_____
_____
_____

7

FOR RENT

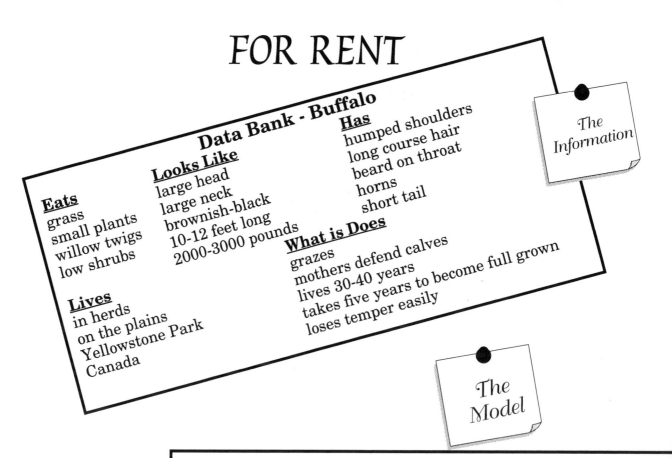

Data Bank - Buffalo

Eats
grass
small plants
willow twigs
low shrubs

Looks Like
large head
large neck
brownish-black
10-12 feet long
2000-3000 pounds

Has
humped shoulders
long course hair
beard on throat
horns
short tail

What is Does
grazes
mothers defend calves
lives 30-40 years
takes five years to become full grown
loses temper easily

Lives
in herds
on the plains
Yellowstone Park
Canada

The Information

The Model

For Rent: One _____

It's the handiest thing ever because it can _____

And _____

And _____

And the greatest thing about it is _____

_____

The Report

For Rent: One buffalo.

It's the handiest thing you'll ever rent since it can

Graze on your lawn to keep it mowed.

Defend you against bullies

And makes a great 2000 pound paperweight

And the greatest thing about it is it lives 30 to 40 years.

THE ATTRIBUTE REPORT

I am frog, come to my home in *ponds, lakes, and rivers.*
I am frog, hear me *croak and plop.*
I am frog, see my *smooth spotted skin,*
see my *big bumpy eyes,*
see my *webbed back feet,*
see my *tiny front fingers.*
I am frog, watch me *jump,*
watch me *swim underwater,*
watch me *catch a fly with my sticky tongue,*
watch me *puff up my chin like a balloon!*
I am frog, hear me, see me, but watch out,
I may be watching you!

I am _____
Come to my home in _____
I am _____
See my _____ Hear me _____
See my _____
See my _____
I am _____
Watch me _____ Watch me _____
Watch me _____
I am _____
I may be watching you.
_____, hear me, see me, but watch out,

Works For Wombats, Too!

I am wombat
Come to my home in Australia
See my long fur
See my sharp claws
See my small ears
I am wombat. Watch me carry my young in a pouch
Watch me dig large earth burrows
Watch me come out only at night
I am wombat, hear me, see me, but watch out,
I may be watching you.

9

THE "IF" REPORT

If I had the feet of a lion
I would have strong, powerful forelegs and
sharp, horny claws to kill small victims with a
single blow
And I'd reach full growth at the age of six and
live about 25 years
But I wouldn't have a horn on my nose
Because a rhinoceros has that.

The Model

If I _____
I would _____
And _____
But I wouldn't _____
Because _____ does that.

You can include a lot of information with this model

If I had the feet of a rhinoceros,
I'd have an odd number of toes on each foot,
And I'd have weak eyesight, but acute hearing and a strong sense of smell,
But I wouldn't be very active at night
Because armadillos do that.

If I had the feet of an armadillo,
I'd use them to burrow underground so that I could escape from my enemies,
And I'd live in South America and the southwest United States,
But I wouldn't ride on my mother's back as a pup
Because a walrus does that.

If I had the feet of a walrus,
I'd rotate my hind feet so that I could move on the ice,
And I'd live on ice floats and ice packs and occasionally sink to the bottom of the ocean to
dig for clams,
But I wouldn't play the game called "This Little Piggie Went To Market",
Because humans do that.

10

THE "CHANGING" REPORT

Use this model to report on an animal or a person, paying particular attention to any changes that occur in the animal or in the person's life. Study the example below:

The Model

You are changing, changing.
You feel: *describe the atmosphere* _____
You are: *two adjectives* _____
You: two verbs or verb phrases _____
You are: *color* _____
the color of: *name something the same color* _____
You are: *give size and shape* _____
And you are: *use participle and prepositional phrase* _____
_____
You do not walk upright anymore as you: *three verb phrases*
_____
It is: adjective to move like this so: *one adjective and one simile*
_____
You are: *name the animal* _____

This is how it looks –

THE WOLF

You are changing, changing.
You feel *a harsh cold wind whip across your face, but you don't mind because*
You are *strong and furry.*
You *sing to the moon* and *roam through the Arctic wilderness without fear and without a map.*
You are *gray,* the *color of fog.*
You are *six feet long from nose to tail tip*
And are *trotting across the Polar Ice Pack toward a distant herd of caribou on shore, your claws clicking with each step you take.*
You do not walk upright anymore,
As you *hunt for snow-white rabbits, lope silently past Polar Bears sniffing the air, and crawl into your home beneath an outcropping of rocks.*
It is *wild* to move like this, so *free* and so *secret like a dream.*
You are an *Arctic Wolf.*

11

You are changing, changing.

You feel _____

_____

You are _____

You _____

_____

You are _____ the color of _____

You are _____

And you are _____

You do not walk upright anymore as you

_____

_____

It is _____
To move like this so
_____
and
_____
You are
_____

12

REPORTING ON

PEOPLE

PEOPLE REPORTS

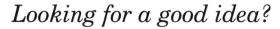

P
E
O
P
L
E

Looking for a good idea?

Try this pattern.

Example:

**THE DAVY CROCKETT
CHANT**

Facts about Crockett: Militia Colonel
Brave hunter   Bold and brave
Sharp-eyed scout   Expert shot
Frontiersman   Told tall tales
Humorist   Married twice
Congressman   Moved four times
From Tennessee   Fought Indians, too.
These are just a few.   From near and far
    Here they are
    Facts about Davy Crockett.

A _____ CHANT

_____

_____

_____

_____

_____

_____

There are just a few.
(Now list seven more facts from the Data Bank)

_____

_____

_____

_____

_____

_____

_____, too!

From near and far
Here they are
Facts about _____.

14

USING PATTERNS

Poems can tell the story!

Davy Crockett
Phone Number Poem

Each line has the number of syllables
in a chosen phone number.

3 Davy at
3 Eight weighed two
4 Hundred pounds with
7 Shoes off, feet clean and no lunch.
6 He could run fast, jump high,
6 Squat lower, dive deeper
6 Than anyone alive.

Davy Crockett
Adverb Poem

1	Adverb	Humbly
2	Adverb	Fearfully
3	Adverb	Hopefully
4	Noun	Davy
5	Verb	Pleads
6	Noun with description	With the angry bear.
7	Any word	"Leave!"

Davy Crockett
Build a Name Poem

D own on the Mississippi
A terrible storm made Davy
V ery mad, so he
Y anked a bolt of lightning from the
sky and rode it!

Five Senses Poem
Davy and the Hollow Tree

Line	
1-Color	The tree was hollow and brown.
2-Sound	It sounded like a bear waking up.
3-Taste	It tasted like fear.
4-Smell	It looked like an animal had slept there.
5-Sight	It looked like a place of danger.
6-Feeling	It made him feel like running.

A Davy Crockett
Limmerick

A frontiersman he was sure enough
So daring, so bold and so tough,
At the old Alamo
He decided to show
That he and his boys could play
rough!

15

THE ASSOCIATIVE LETTER REPORT!

What letter can you associate with a famous person? Look at how C is for Tiny Tim. Each word beginning with C could be a fully illustrated page with more text about him. You can use the same idea to create a book about any real or literary person.

Example

– C Is For Tiny Tim (from Dicken's A Christmas Carol) –

C IS FOR CHRISTMAS
The famous story which features Tiny Tim as one of its characters takes place during the CHRISTMAS season.

C IS FOR CRUTCH
Tiny Tim had to walk with a CRUTCH or be carried by his father.

C IS FOR CRATCHIT
Tiny Tim's last name was CRATCHIT.

C IS FOR CHEERFUL
No matter what, Tiny Tim was always CHEERFUL.

C IS FOR CRUEL
Tiny Tim lived in a CRUEL city where only the rich could afford doctors.

C IS FOR CAUTIOUS
Tiny Tim's parents were CAUTIOUS about predicting his future.

C IS FOR CRIPPLED
Tiny Tim could not walk.

B Is For Rosa Parks

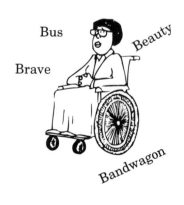

Bus
Beauty
Brave
Bandwagon

R Is For Einstein

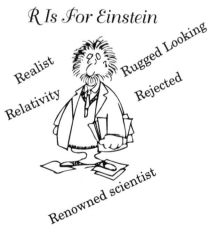

Realist
Relativity
Rugged Looking
Rejected
Renowned scientist

I Is For Benjamin Franklin

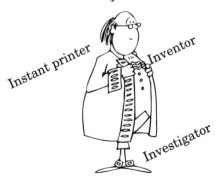

Instant printer
Inventor
Investigator

16

THE ACROSTIC

This acrostic describes one incident in Churchill's life when he was 19-years-old.

W   ar correspondent
I   n South Africa, 1899
N   ortorious Boer enemy
S   eizes armored
T   rain
O   f those aboard, he is captured.
N   o hope of escape.

C   hecks out prison camp.
H   igh walls, floodlights, sentries.
U   p, over the wall, in an unguarded moment
R   acing heart, he scales the heights.
C   amp left behind.
H   opping railroad cars
I   n dead of night finds British help.
L   auded as a hero.
L   eader of the future.

A ripping good way to summarize!

17

THE BIO POEM

A bio-poem is one way to briefly tell about someone's life. Here is an example.

Abraham

Tall, thin, lanky, bearded,

Son of Nancy and Tom, husband of Mary Todd, father of Robert, Edward, Willie and Tad.

Who cares deeply about all men,

Who feels sad much of the time, sometimes alone in the world,

Who needs to win the hearts of <u>all</u> his countrymen,

Who gives love to his family, advice to his generals, consolation to a sorrowing nation,

Who fears the dissolution of the American union,

Who would like to see every man respected for his God-given dignity,

Resident of 1600 Pennsylvania Avenue, Washington, D. C.

18

BIO POEMS ARE

FUN TO WRITE!

PEOPLE

Now try one of your own!

Select a person whose biography you have read and follow the pattern given below.

Line 1 - Name   _____

Line 2 - Four traits   _____

Line 3 - Related to   _____

Line 4 - Who cares deeply about   _____

Line 5 - Who feels   _____

Line 6 - Who needs   _____

Line 7 - Who gives   _____

Line 8 - Who fears   _____

Line 9 - Who would like to see   _____

Line 10 - Resident of   _____

MYSTERY PERSON REPORT

Directions:

1. Read a biography about the person you select.

2. List ten facts about the person. Do not put the facts in any kind of order.

3. Ask: "Who would like to play the mystery person game?" Tell your classmates that (one at a time) they may give you a number between one and ten. You can read the clue for that number. The person selecting the number can then guess who the person is or pass. Classmates continue giving numbers and hearing the clues until the mystery person's identity is guessed or all clues have been read.

4. Be sue to tell those playing the game that if one thinks he knows the mystery person's identity and it is not his/her turn, to please *not call out* the answer. Simply raise your hand to select the next number.

MYSTERY PERSON REPORT

1. I always wanted to be an actor and spent some time on the stage.

2. I am not a citizen of the United States.

3. My writings have been translated into more languages than any other book except the Bible.

4. I left home to seek my fortune at the age of fourteen.

5. I wrote *The Ugly Duckling* and *The Little Mermaid*.

6. I often met with failure.

7. I was an honored guest of kings.

8. My father supported us by mending shoes.

9. I consider my plays to be my best work.

10. I was a lonely child and spent a lot of time on the docks with the fishmongers.

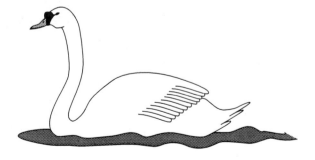

The mystery person is Hans Christian Andersen

LIKE MUSIC? WRITE A SONG!

A SONG ABOUT JEAN LAFFITE
(Sing to the tune of "Oh, Susannah.")

(1)
Oh he comes from Barataria,
And his name is Jean Laffite,
Bold and brave New Orleans' pirate,
When the other ships he'd meet.

CHORUS:
When he plundered
Both French and Spanish ships
He would be both bold and daring,
With a smile upon his lips.

(2)
When the British offered money,
If their cause he chose to aid,
He then fought for his own country,
And did not want to be paid.

(3)
Went to Galveston with all his men,
Resumed his pirate ways,
So no ship was safe from Jean Laffite,
The rest of all his days.

Here's a song about the adventures of one of the early trappers. Sing it to the tune of "Oh, Susannah".

Oh, a hunter and a trapper,
A fur trader and a guide,
Yes, he crossed the rocky mountains
With his rifle at his side.

Chorus
    Built Fort Bridger
    So folks could find their way,
    Oh, Jim Bridger was a mountain man
    Always on his way.

Oh, for forty years moved onward
Leaving mountains in his wake
Was the first to gaze upon it
The magnificent Salt Lake.

22

WRITE IT AND PERFORM IT

The Biography Report: The "To Tell the Truth" Show

The report that follows is done as a television game show. Three persons are pretending to be Jim Bowie. Only one is the real Jim Bowie and always tells the truth. The other two make a number of false statements.

Class members can read the speaking parts. The entire class can vote on the person they think is the real Jim Bowie.

Choose another famous person and write a TV show script similar to the one that follows. Use the Jim Bowie script as your model.

HOST OR HOSTESS: LARRY OR LORETTA BORE

Welcome everyone to the "To Tell the Truth" Show! Our three guests all claim to be the famous Jim Bowie. Only one, however is telling the complete truth. It is up to you to decide which is the real Jim Bowie. Now let's meet our guests. Jim Bowie number one would you tell us your story.

JIM BOWIE #1

I was born in Georgia in 1799 and was always big for my age. The first twenty-nine years of my life I moved around a lot but finally settled in Texas in 1828.

JIM BOWIE #2

I was born in Texas in 1799 but left Texas to settle for a spell in Alabama and Mississippi. I lived a rough life, pirating with Jean Lafitte and fighting Indians. I was even shot once in a gun fight.

JIM BOWIE #3

I was born in Louisiana in 1799 and lived a pretty rough life. In an Indian fight I lost my grip on the butcher knife in my hand and that's why I invented the Bowie Knife.

LARRY OR LORETTA BORE:

What else can you tell us about yourselves.

JIM BOWIE #1

I felt that Texans should be free so I fought in the Texas resistance movement at Nacodoches in 1832 and, of course, lost my life at the Alamo in 1836.

JIM BOWIE #2

I lived in Texas all my life which is why I fought so hard for freedom. It was my bad luck to be so sick when Santa Anna attacked the Alamo that I could not fight as hard as I wanted to.

JIM BOWIE #3

I was a prospector and a land speculator hoping to make my fortune in Texas lands. I never fought Indians but I did fight in the Texas resistance movement.

LARRY OR LORETTA BORE:

Now it is time to decide which of our guests it the real Jim Bowie. We will vote by a show of hands. Is it number one? Is it number two? Is it number three? Now for the moment you have all been waiting for. Will the real Jim Bowie, inventor of the Bowie Knife and defender of freedom at the Alamo please step forward.

(Answer: Number one. Both two and three contradicted themselves.)

23

To Tell the Truth

Person: _____

Script:

Host or Hostess

_____

_____

_____

#1

_____

_____

_____

#2

_____

_____

#3

_____

_____

_____

HOST/HOSTESS

_____

_____

_____

#1

_____

_____

_____

#2

_____

_____

#3

_____

_____

HOST/HOSTESS

_____

_____

Answer

_____

24

REPORTING ON

PLACES

IF I SPENT THE NIGHT IN ...

List what you would see in a particular place at night. Use the items in your list to complete the pattern.

If I spent the night in _____

I would see _____

If I spent the night in _____

I would see _____

(and) _____

and _____

but I wouldn't see _____

because that happens in _____

If I spent the night in the *Ozarks* I would see *a great horned owl sitting like a wide-eyed sentinel in a huge oak tree, a pale-eyed opossum scavenging the forest floor for scraps of food and a sharp-eyed fox stealing its way through the shadows while prowling for a late night supper*, but I wouldn't see *a brush-tailed wambenger stealing eggs from a bird's nest* because that happens in *the Australian Outback*.

WRITE A POEM ABOUT A STATE

Use these patterns to report on a state, country or province. Study the examples below, then write a poem following one of the models. Be sure to include accurate information about the place you choose. You should have a note card to show where you got the information.

Five Senses Poem

Line
1-Color	California is yellow as the sun.
2-Sound	It sounds like the surf pounding.
3-Taste	It tastes like fresh oranges.
4-Smell	It smells like sea salt.
5-Sight	It looks like an ocean shadowed by mountains and palm trees.
6-Feeling	It makes me feel like playing.

**State
Build a Name Poem**

U	ndeveloped land
T	reeless in many places
A	wesome Salt Lake
H	as many copper mines.

**State
Adverb Poem**

1	Adverb	Abruptly
2	Adverb	Majestically
3	Adverb	Proudly
4	Noun	The Blue Ridge Mountains
5	Verb	Cover
6	Noun with description	The western edge
7	Any word	of Virginia

**State
Phone Number Poem**

Each line has the number of syllables in a chosen phone number.

3	French trappers
3	and traders
4	explored this state
7	prospectors discovered gold
6	in 1862
6	bringing many settlers
9	and statehood in 1884

Montana

27

THE MYSTERY PLACE REPORT

Where am I?

Create a **Mystery Place** game by listing ten clues about a country, province, state or city. One clue must be a "give-away" clue.

Here are clues for the country of EGYPT.
1. The official language of this country is Arabic.
2. This country is almost square in shape.
3. The Mediterranean Sea forms the northern boundary of this country.
4. The Nile River runs through this country.
5. The capital of this country is Cairo.
6. This country has a very dry climate and rain seldom falls.
7. The Great Sphinx can be found in this country.
8. This country was granted independence from Britain in 1922.
9. This country was invaded by Germany in 1940.
10. The name of this country begins with an E and ends with a T.

Play the **Mystery Place** game with your class. A student selects a number between one and ten. You read the clue for that number and the student can guess the name of the country or pass. If the student does not guess correctly, then another student chooses a number and you read the clue for that number. Continue until the place is guessed or all clues are read.

28

THE MYSTERY STATE REPORT

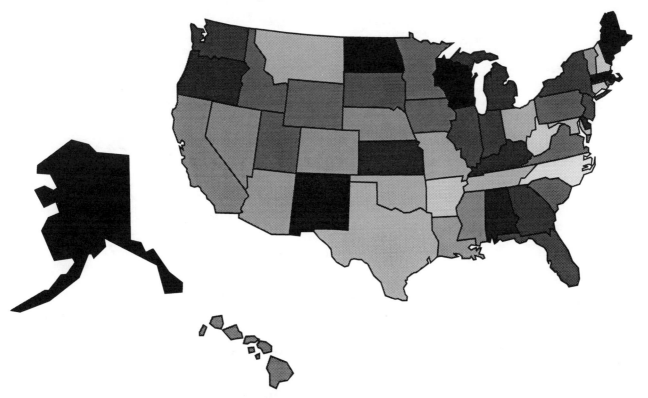

Clues for one of the fifty states.

1. Somewhere in this state is a huge statue of Paul Bunyan and his blue ox, Babe.

2. Canoeing is a favorite pastime of many people in this state.

3. This state is 12th in area size of all the states.

4. A lot of breakfast cereal comes from this state.

5. The state bird is the goldfinch.

6. The first white men arrived in the land which is now this state in the 1650s.

7. This is known as the Gopher State.

8. The capital of this state is St. Paul.

9. This territory became a state in 1858.

10. This has been a state for more than 100 years.

Answer: Minnesota

SING IT!

Choose a country and find the capital and a large city. Now find some things that are manufactured there and some crops that are grown there. Fill in the blanks in the song below. Sing it to your class to the tune of "She'll Be Coming Around the Mountain."

Country _____

Capital _____

Large City _____

Manufactured Goods _____

Crops _____

Example:

She'll be coming from <u>Buenos Aires</u> (capital)when she comes,

She'll be coming from <u>Cordoba</u> (large city)when she comes,

She'll bring <u>soap and iron and steel </u>(three products)

She'll bring <u>corn and cotton and sugar cane</u> (three crops)

She'll be coming from <u>Argentina</u> when she comes.

30

IF I VISITED ...

Use the model below to compare two or more places. Be sure to include information that will clearly identify each place.

Example

If I visited <u>Missouri</u>

I would <u>climb the Ozark Mountains</u>

And <u>ride a riverboat on the Mississippi</u>

But I wouldn't <u>visit Lincoln's birthplace or throw</u>

<u>pebbles in Lake Michigan</u>

Because only visitors to <u>Illinois</u>

Do that.

Your turn

If I visited _____

I would _____

And _____

But I wouldn't _____

_____

Or _____

Because only visitors to _____

Do that.

31

THE ALLITERATIVE PARAGRAPH

Select a topic. Read about the topic. Take notes on information you find particularly interesting. Write one or more alliterative paragraphs about your topic. (As many words as possible must begin with the first letter of your topic.)

UTAH

Until recently Utah was understood to be one of the unlikely areas for urban development. The state was unaffected by ultra-modern undertakings because most were uncertain how to use the unusual and unique land.

Unfettered by unsavory speculators the unspotted Uinta Mountains remain a utopia for wildlife. Utilization of the unequaled landscape will unlock its ultimate beauty. Those unaware of the unbridled fury of unleashed desert storms will find the land unsuitable, leaving this unruly state to its upright citizens.

FACT OR FICTION BOOKS

Fact or Fiction?

For hundreds of years Russia was called "the sleeping bear of the world."

Fact

Long after other countries had modern factories, the people of Russia were still farmers, using the same hand tools their ancestors used to till the land. There were no modern factories until the 1900s.

Make your own fact or fiction book about a place.

1. On one page you make a statement about the place and ask your reader if the statement is fact or fiction.

2. On the next page you tell your reader whether the statement is fact or fiction and why.

3. Your book can have as many pages as you wish.

33

FACT

FACT OR FICTION?

REPORTING ON

EVENTS

THE "HISTORY RIDDLE" REPORT

PLACES and EVENTS

LET'S GO TO LONG AGO PLACES AND SEE HISTORY'S CHANGING FACES:

A crowded beach with the muck and stink of smoke overhead

With bullets and bombs behind and above

And off shore, the Kentish Maid

But no way to get to the boat.

Then a destroyer comes up with ack ack and pom poms

And between bullets they come

Small boats of every description

BUT THAT'S NOT ALL

From 100 miles across the North Sea

They sailed through water and shell

To get the men off the beaches

The wounded went first

Some died so others could escape

Beaten but unconquered

They faced the enemy

And democracy shone in all its splendor

WHERE AM I?

DUNKIRK, OF COURSE

LET'S GO TO LONG AGO PLACES

AND SEE HISTORY'S CHANGING FACES:

(List eight things you would see)

_____

_____

_____

_____

_____

_____

_____

_____

BUT THAT'S NOT ALL

(List eight more sights)

_____

_____

_____

_____

_____

_____

_____

_____

WHERE AM I?

_____, OF COURSE

36

A DEVASTATING DIAMANTE

The diamante is used here to describe the destruction of the city of Coventry in England during one night in World War II.

Coventry
Air raid
Blackout, fire, bombs
Stukas, Hitler's terror birds
Home guard helpless
Fire everywhere
Devastation

_____

_____

_____

_____

_____

_____

You can use the same pattern to describe any other event.

THE "WHAT EVER HAPPENED TO" REPORT

EVENTS

Here is a model for reporting on unexplained events.

THE MODEL:
WHAT EVER HAPPENED TO Amelia Earhart?
DID SHE crash in the Pacific Ocean in 1937?
MAYBE SHE landed on an island where she now lives secretly and alone
OR COULD IT BE THAT she was captured by the Japanese and shot because they thought she was a spy?
WAS THERE a typhoon that blew her plane off course?
MAYBE SOMEDAY WE WILL KNOW the truth about her disappearance and find that she works for the airmail division of the U.S. Postal Service!

Keith Polette

USE THIS MODEL to report on another unexplained event.
EXAMPLE:
WHAT EVER HAPPENED TO THE PASSENGER PIGEON?
OR
WHAT EVER HAPPENED TO THE DINOSAURS?

THE PATTERN
WHAT EVER HAPPENED TO

_____

DID (HE, SHE, IT, THEY)

_____

MAYBE (HE, SHE, IT, THEY)

_____

OR COULD IT BE THAT _____

_____

WAS THERE A

_____

THAT _____
MAYBE SOMEDAY _____

38

THE "ONLY ONE" REPORT

THE ALAMO

San Antonio, Texas has many buildings

But ONLY ONE ALAMO

In 1836 the Alamo was attacked by 6000 men

In ONLY ONE ARMY.

The attacking army had many officers

But ONLY ONE GENERAL.

The Alamo was defended by 182 men

With ONLY ONE PURPOSE

Travis, the Texan's leader sent many pleas for help

But ONLY ONE RELIEF PARTY responded

Both sides wanted to win the battle

But there was ONLY ONE OUTCOME

There are many events to remember in Texas history,

But ONLY ONE ALAMO.

Still more patterns!!

Try these models for reporting research on historical events

THE "IF I HAD" PATTERN

If I had the power of a Chinese Emperor
I would build a great wall to protect my people
And I would make it 1500 miles long
But I wouldn't build a mission in Texas
Because Father Olivares did that.

IF I HAD

If I had the courage of _____

_____

I would _____

_____

And I would _____

_____

But I wouldn't _____

_____

Because _____

_____ did that.

39

THE "YOU WERE THERE" REPORT

San Francisco Gold Rush Days

One <u>fog filled</u> (morning/evening) <u>as the ocean mist permeated the air </u>(describe the weather) <u>the sound of sea gulls screeched across the bay </u>(tell how it awakens you) and awakens you. Sounds of <u>pounding hammers </u>(what) from <u>builders of wooden shacks </u>(where) beckon you, "come out, come out."

You dress quickly, race down the stairs and throw open the door. Outside everything is different. You look down at your clothing. You, too, are different. You are a child of <u>1880</u> (year).

Your <u>homespun shirt </u>(describe your clothing) <u>scratches your skin </u>(tell how the clothing feels). You hurry <u>down to Fisherman's Wharf </u>(tell where you are going) You hear <u>the slap of nets against the sides of fishing boats</u>. You see <u>passenger ships rotting and abandoned from the gold.</u> You smell <u>the leavings of raw fish.</u> A feeling of <u>adventure</u> overcomes you. You look up at <u>a handsome gentleman who approaches </u>(what) and catch your breath as you see <u>James J. Brown</u> (who). He/she <u>struck it rich in the 50s with gold</u> (describe this famous person) and <u>lives in a huge mansion on the hill. He turns to his well-dressed wife, Molly</u> (tell something the person does) Everyone listens to his/her words "<u>Don't worry if society folks won't accept us. We can buy and sell most of them</u>". The people around <u>the Browns</u> (tell how they react) <u>turn up their noses at them.</u> A great feeling of <u>anger against prejudice</u> overwhelms you, lifts you up and carries you back to the door of your home. You open the door and step inside. The world of <u>1880</u> (year) fades to the past and you are once again a child of the 1990s.

40

THE PATTERN

One _____ (morning/evening)

_____
(describe the weather)

_____
(tell how it awakens you)
and awakens you. Sounds of _____
(what)

from _____
(where)
beckon you, "come out, come out."
You dress quickly, race down the stairs and
throw open the door. Outside everything is
different. You look down at your clothing. You,
too, are different. You are a child of _____
(year)

Your _____
(describe your clothing)

_____
(tell how the clothing feels)
You hurry_____
(tell where you are going)

_____
You hear _____
You see _____
You smell _____
A feeling of _____ overcomes you.
You look up at _____(what)
and catch your breath as you see _____
(who)

He/she _____
(describe this famous person)
and _____
(tell something the person does)
Everyone listens to his/her words "_____
_____ ".
The people around _____
(tell how they react)

_____.
A great feeling of _____ overwhelms you,
lifts you up and carries you back to the door of
your home. You open the door and step inside.
The world of _____ (year) fades to the past and
you are once again a child of the 1990s.

41

I WONDER WHY ...

I WONDER WHY....

   THEY

   Contour the fields

   Plant the "suckers"

   Spray and weed

   Pick and load

   Peel and cut

   Trim and grade

   Pack in cans

   Ship to market

   And advertise special sales on

PINEAPPLES

When I could have an apple

instead!

I WONDER WHY....

   THEY

_____

_____

_____

_____

_____

_____

_____

_____

When I could _____

instead!

I WONDER WHY...

   THEY

   Captured slaves

   Made them work

   Digging clay

   Mixing with water

   Baking bricks

   Piling on carts

   Pulling to the wall

   Setting with lime

   Building towers

   Burying bodies

   Dropping with exhaustion

When they could talk peace

instead.

I WONDER WHY....

   THEY

_____

_____

_____

_____

_____

_____

_____

_____

When I could _____

instead!

42

SO YOU DON'T LIKE TO WRITE!

Try: The Newspaper Clipping Report

Select a topic. This can be on a current event or a general topic.

Here are topics to think about.

Aircraft	New Ideas
Business	Olympic Games
Conservation	Propaganda
Disasters	Quasars
Earth-Our-Home	Record-Setting Events
Funny Happenings	Space
Great Performances	Technology
Human Interest Stories	Unusual Events
Interesting People	Victories
Joyful Moments	Water
Keepers of Freedom	X-Rays and Other Medical
Law and Order	Miracles
Misunderstandings	Youthful Accomplishments
	Zealots

43

NEWSPAPER CLIPPING REPORT

TECHNOLOGY

Find a picture, name or article about these—add other items

1. An energy producer
2. Something a computer expert might use
3. An invention to use in your home
4. An industry that might pollute
5. An example of mass transportation
6. Someone to write about an environmental concern
7. A product that might pollute
8. Someone's opinion of technology
9. A technological job opening
10. Technology in the kitchen

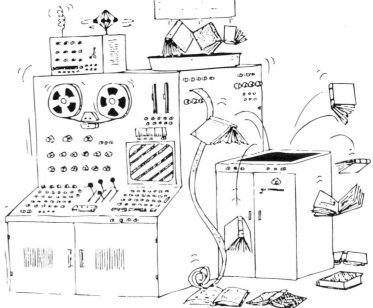

Sample Items

TOPIC: KEEPERS OF FREEDOM

1. A picture that symbolizes freedom.
2. A Patriotic headline.
3. An article about loss of freedom.
4. An event that could take place only in a free society.
5. A statement concerning freedom of speech.
6. A controversial topic.
7. The name of one who can do something about injustice.
8. The name of a female leader.

Putting it all together!

Watch your newspaper for ads, photographs, cartoons and features related to the subject you choose.

Begin clipping!
Sort your clippings into major subject headings...this can be by date or by type of feature or other headings you choose.
Display for others to see:

       in a book

       on the bulletin board

       or other display